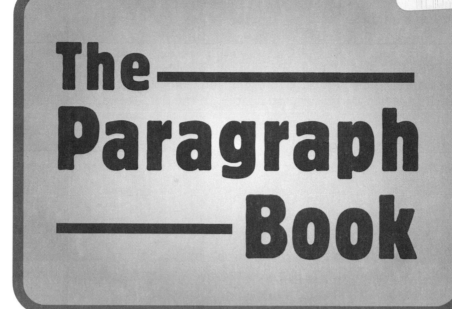

The Paragraph Book

BOOK 1:
Writing the How-to Paragraph

Dianne Tucker-LaPlount

Educators Publishing Service
Cambridge and Toronto

THANK YOU

Thanks to all my students through the years who taught me all I know about teaching paragraph writing.

Thanks to the students of Sue Wallace's reading lab and summer classes at Home Street Middle School, Bishop, California; Eva Poole-Gilson's English class at High Desert Academy, Benton, California; and Cindy Donaldson's class at Carson Literacy Center in San Diego for participating in the field testing of this work.

A special thank-you to Amber Keppler of High Desert for her How-to Paragraph, titled *How to Groom a Horse*, and the How-to Essay that she developed from that paragraph.

Illustrations by Steve Sullivan, represented by Creative Freelancers
Design by Persis Barron Levy
Editor: Ilie Ruby
Managing Editor: Sheila Neylon

Printed in U.S.A.
ISBN 0-8388-2671-7

3 4 5 6 7 VGP 08 07 06 05 04

TO THE STUDENT

Most birds don't drink water like animals do. So...how do birds drink? To find out, read the paragraph below. (And you will also find out how this book works.)

How to Drink Water If You Happen to Be a Song Sparrow

First, you dip your beak into a puddle of clean water. Next, you fill your mouth with water. Then, you lift your head high with your beak open. Finally, you let the water flow down your throat.

O.K., so you're not a song sparrow, but anything you know how to do, from changing a light bulb to adding more memory to a computer, can be put into writing, using the simple FNTF Formula: *First, . . . Next, . . . Then, . . . Finally, ...*

This book is about using the FNTF formula to write easily and clearly.

Is good writing important? Of course! Good writing helps you express yourself. It leads to higher grades and better jobs. It sharpens your thinking and makes reading easier and more fun. Most of all, it gives you a sense of confidence and satisfaction.

Don't be surprised if you find your concentration and your memory improving as your writing develops. You'll see a gain in your comprehension of written material as well, and reading will become more interesting.

This book will help you get started. It is the first in a series of four books on paragraph writing. Keep in mind that you may not become a prize-winning writer immediately, but if you take it one step at a time, you'll be on your way! *First, . . . Next, . . . Then, . . . Finally, ...*

TABLE OF CONTENTS

LESSON 1: GIVING INSTRUCTIONS

▲▲ THE HOW-TO PARAGRAPH ▲▲▲▲▲▲▲▲▲▲▲▲▲▲▲▲

▼ A paragraph is like a family. In a family, all the members are related. In a paragraph, all the sentences are related.

Below are two groups of sentences. One group is a paragraph; the other is not.

A. *A baby humpback whale is 15 feet long when it is born. That's about as long as a car. Sewing buttons on a shirt is difficult. The wind blew the screen door off the porch.*

B. *Dragonflies are among the world's fastest insects. Many dragonflies can fly at speeds up to 30 miles per hour. Their wings beat so fast that they can appear perfectly still in the air.*

Which group of sentences is a paragraph, A. or B.?

If you picked B., the second group, you're correct because all the sentences in that group are closely related.

▼ A paragraph should have a single **topic**. The topic is what the paragraph is mainly about.

Choose the correct answer. In the second group of sentences above, the topic is

      a. why dragons have wings.

      b. the eating habits of dragonflies.

      c. how fast dragonflies can fly.

THE FNTF FORMULA ▲▲▲▲▲▲▲▲▲▲▲▲▲▲▲▲▲▲▲▲▲▲▲▲

COOKING UP A PARAGRAPH

▼ A formula is like a recipe. It tells how to put something together the same way every time.

A recipe is useful for cooking or baking. A formula is useful when you're writing a paragraph. How?

When you can't think of anything to say, the words of the formula help you get started.

You don't have to worry about organizing your paragraph. The words of the formula do it for you.

This lesson will show you how to use a formula to create a How-to Paragraph. A How-to Paragraph is a paragraph that gives instructions. It tells how to do something.

Here is the formula for writing a How-to Paragraph:

> *First, . . .*
>
> *Next, . . .*
>
> *Then, . . .*
>
> *Finally, ...*

▼ Memorize this formula: *First, . . . Next, . . . Then, . . . Finally, ...*

You will use it again and again. It is called the FNTF formula:
First, . . . Next, . . . Then, . . . Finally, . . .

Say the words out loud to fix them in your memory: *First, . . . Next, . . . Then, . . . Finally, ...*

A HOW-TO PARAGRAPH: EXAMINE CAREFULLY

Here's an example of a How-to Paragraph. Read the paragraph and look closely at how it is put together. See if you can answer the questions below.

How to Open a Jar of Pickles

First, place the jar of pickles on a counter. Next, hold the jar with one hand and grasp the lid with the other hand. Then, turn the lid until it is loose. Finally, lift the lid off the jar.

1. What is the title of this paragraph?

   _____

2. Why is this paragraph called a How-to Paragraph?

   _____

   _____

3. The purpose of the paragraph is to give instructions on how to open a jar of pickles. Can you tell the paragraph's purpose just by reading the title?

   _____

4. How many sentences does the paragraph have?

   _____

5. The formula for writing a How-to Paragraph is FNTF (*First, . . . Next, . . . Then, . . . Finally, . . .*). Does this paragraph use the FNTF formula?

   _____

6. Are the formula words in the correct order?

   _____

7. Which word does the first sentence start with? _____

8. What punctuation mark comes after that word? _____

9. Which three other words in the paragraph have a comma after them?

   _____   _____   _____

The writer of the paragraph on page 5 was given the title: *How to Open a Jar of Pickles*. He made a list of words that came to mind before he started writing the paragraph. He ended up using all of the words except *put* and *cover*. He organized his information in a flow chart using the FNTF formula.

Word List:

put	hold	grasp	turn	lift
place	with one hand	cover	until	off
counter	the other hand	lid	loose	

Title:

> How to Open a Jar of Pickles

FIRST:

> place jar on counter

↓

NEXT:

> grasp lid

↓

THEN:

> turn lid until loose

↓

FINALLY:

> lift lid off

THE COMPLETE PARAGRAPH

The writer then wrote the paragraph on another piece of paper, like this:

How to Open a Jar of Pickles

First, place the jar of pickles on a counter. Next, hold the jar with one hand and grasp the lid with the other hand. Then, turn the lid until it is loose. Finally, lift the lid off the jar.

In four sentences, he produced a complete, well-written paragraph.

WHO IS YOUR AUDIENCE? ▲▲▲▲▲▲▲▲▲▲▲▲▲▲▲▲▲▲▲▲▲▲▲▲▲▲

In other words, whom are you writing your paragraph for?

▼ A How-to Paragraph tells how to do something: how to use a telephone, how to fix a flat tire on a bike, even how to pop a balloon.

When you write a How-to Paragraph, make your instructions clear and simple.

Think of the person who will read your paragraph. Pretend that your reader is someone who knows nothing about phones or bicycles or balloons.

For example, pretend you are giving instructions to a visitor from the past. Let's say this person lived thousands of years ago. She comes from a time when people lived in caves and made their tools from stones and bones. Let's call her Ms. Pebble.

This Stone Age time traveler can capture giant mammoths. She can rub sticks together to make fire. She can decorate the walls of a cave. But she has no idea how people in our society do even the simplest things.

Pretend our visitor doesn't know how to open a jar of pickles.

She has never changed a light bulb.

She even needs to be told how to turn on a faucet to get a glass of water.

You're going to have to make your instructions clear and simple if you want this Stone Age stranger to understand them.

🖎 **ASSIGNMENT 1**   Your teacher will give you your paragraph-writing assignment sheet. It tells you the title and what to do.

Before you begin, study the vocabulary words on the next page. They go with your paragraph title. You can use the vocabulary words to help you as you write your paragraph. You don't have to use all the words. Choose words of your own, if you like. A flow chart is there to help you get started. You can fill in the flow chart by thinking about your instructions in steps.

VOCABULARY for Paragraph 1: How to Get a Glass of Water

glass	kitchen
faucet	sink
running	turn

Now how do I get a glass of water?

Title:

FIRST:

↓

NEXT:

↓

THEN:

↓

FINALLY:

REVIEW OF LESSON 1

Circle the letter in front of the correct answer.

1. A paragraph is a group of sentences that are closely related. Read the two groups of sentences below. Which group is a paragraph?

    a. In New Mexico, there is a mountain of rock almost 300 feet high called Sky City. The mountain is flat on top. Native Americans have lived in this tiny city on top of a mountain for over 800 years.

    b. When the toast burns, our smoke alarm goes off. For best results, tomato plants need plenty of sunshine and water. An alligator can go for many months without eating.

2. A formula is like a

    a. recipe.

    b. cake.

    c. smoke alarm.

    d. puddle of water.

3. A How-to Paragraph tells

    a. a story.

    b. how to do something.

    c. about your feelings.

    d. about time-travelers.

4. The order of words in the FNTF formula is

    a. *First, . . . Next, . . . Then, . . . Finally, . . .*

    b. *First, . . . Then, . . . Next, . . . Finally, . . .*

    c. *First, . . . Finally, . . . Then, . . . Finally, . . .*

    d. *First, . . . Finally, . . . Next, . . . Then, . . .*

5. The FNTF formula is used in writing a

    a. word.

    b. letter.

    c. sentence.

    d. How-to Paragraph.

6. The purpose of a How-to Paragraph is to

   a. tell a story.

   b. give instructions.

   c. invite someone to an event.

   d. announce an event.

7. You can tell the purpose of a How-to Paragraph as soon as you read the

   a. paragraph.

   b. last line.

   c. title.

   d. first word.

8. When you write a How-to Paragraph, pretend you are giving instructions to someone from the past. This will help you make the instructions in your paragraph

   a. clear.

   b. long.

   c. confusing.

   d. disorganized.

9. A topic is

   a. the top of the page.

   b. what the paragraph is mainly about.

   c. the first sentence of a paragraph.

   d. the last sentence of a paragraph.

Number correct: _____ out of 9

Lesson 1 QUIZ Now your teacher will give you the quiz for Lesson 1.

YOUR HOW-TO PARAGRAPH

LESSON 2: FORMAT

▲▲ FORMAT: HOW IT LOOKS ON THE PAGE ▲▲▲▲▲

The word **edit** means to check and correct.

When you finish writing a paragraph, edit the paragraph. Read it carefully, check for mistakes, and make corrections if necessary.

This writing program shows how to edit five elements of a paragraph:

> (1) format
>
> (2) capitalization and punctuation
>
> (3) subjects
>
> (4) verbs
>
> (5) thought

The aim is to help you spot and correct your writing mistakes quickly and easily.

▼ We begin with **format**. Format deals with how a paragraph looks on the page. This includes the arrangement and spacing of the title and the sentences.

FORMATTING A PARAGRAPH TWO WAYS ▲▲▲▲▲▲

This is how a correctly formatted handwritten paragraph looks.

How to Bathe an Elephant

First, you get a well-trained elephant. Next, you tie one end of a long rope around the elephant's neck. Then, you pick up the loose end of the rope and lead the elephant into a pond. Finally, you stand far back and watch the big fellow spray himself with his trunk.

 If you're using a keyboard, the paragraph should look like this:

How to Bathe an Elephant

First, you get a well-trained elephant. Next, you tie one end of a long rope around the elephant's neck. Then, you pick up the loose end of the rope and lead the elephant into a pond. Finally, you stand far back and watch the big fellow spray himself with his trunk.

FORMAT: WHAT TO LOOK FOR

▼ Here is what you find if a paragraph is formatted correctly.

1. **The title is centered above the paragraph.**
   Centered is another way of saying placed in the center.

2. **There is a blank line after the title line.**

3. **The first line of the paragraph is indented.**
   To indent a line means to begin a line with a blank space.
   The space should be about the width of your thumb.

4. **Each new sentence begins right after the sentence before it.**

5. **After the first line, each new line starts at the left margin.**

A **margin** is a blank border around the print on a page. The left margin can also mean the vertical red line about one inch from the left edge of a sheet of lined paper. (Vertical is up and down.)

The left margin is not found on all lined paper. Sometimes it is not there. You just have to pretend it is!

6. **The right margin is uncrowded.** This means that words at the end of a line aren't bunched up against the right edge of the paper.

Why bother with formatting rules? The answer is simple: they make the paragraph easy to look at and read.

▼ Read this How-to Paragraph. Then, ask yourself the questions below it. You will find that the paragraph contains one or more mistakes in format.

	How to Ride a Skateboard
	First, you place your skateboard on the
	ground with the wheels down. Next, you put one foot
	on the skateboard.
	Then, you push off the ground with the other foot
	until you're moving. Finally, you balance and ride.

USE THESE QUESTIONS TO CHECK FOR FORMAT MISTAKES

▼ Ask yourself

1. Is the title centered over the paragraph above? _____

2. Is there a blank line after the title line? _____

3. Is the first line of the paragraph indented? _____

4. Does each new sentence begin right after the sentence before it? _____

5. After the first line, does each new line start at the left margin? _____

6. Is there space between the end of each line and the right edge of the paper? In other words, is the right margin uncrowded? _____

You're correct if you wrote *No* to questions 2, 4, and 6, and *Yes* to 1, 3, and 5. Go to the next page to see how format corrections are made with the help of editing marks.

HOW DO I MAKE FORMAT CORRECTIONS?

Editing marks are used for correcting mistakes in written material. Here is how to correct the format mistakes in *How to Ride a Skateboard*.

How to Ride a Skateboard   #

First, you place your skateboard on the

ground with the wheels down. Next, you put one foot

on the skateboard.   #

Then, you push off the ground with the other foot

until you're moving. Finally, you balance and ride.

A space mark **#** shows that a space is needed between title and first line.

An arrow ← shows where the third sentence should be moved so that it follows immediately after the second sentence.

Again, a space mark **#** shows that more space is needed. The end of the second line of the paragraph is crowding the right edge of the paper.

▼ Below is the same How-to Paragraph with two different format mistakes. Can you spot them?

VERSION 2

	How to Ride a Skateboard
	First, you place your skateboard on the ground
	with the wheels down. Next, you put one foot on the
	skateboard. Then, you push off the ground with the other
	foot until you're moving. Finally, you balance and ride.

Notice that the title is not centered. Also, the first line is not indented. Turn the page to see how the corrections are made.

Two new editing marks are introduced to make corrections on Version 2.

VERSION 2 CORRECTIONS

	]How to Ride a Skateboard[
	⌊First, you place your skateboard on the ground
	with the wheels down. Next, you put one foot on the
	skateboard. Then, you push off the ground with the other
	foot until you're moving. Finally, you balance and ride.

Reverse brackets] [show that the title should be centered.

A mark that looks like a large capital ⌊ shows that the first line should be indented. (Another way of showing this is ¶.)

▼ Here is the same paragraph, this time with another kind of format mistake. Can you spot it? (The same mistake happens twice.)

VERSION 3

	How to Ride a Skateboard
	First, you place your skateboard on the ground with the
	wheels down. Next, you put one foot on the skateboard. Then,
	you push off the ground with the other foot until
	you're moving. Finally, you balance and ride.

Notice that the last two lines do not begin at the left margin. The lines have "drifted" away from the margin. The corrections are below.

VERSION 3 CORRECTIONS

	How to Ride a Skateboard
	First, you place your skateboard on the ground with the
	wheels down. Next, you put one foot on the skateboard. Then,
	← *you push off the ground with the other foot until*
	←— *you're moving. Finally, you balance and ride.*

The third and fourth lines have drifted away from the left margin. An arrow ←— shows where each line should begin.

START A LIST OF EDITING MARKS

▼ On a lined 4" x 6" blue card, copy the four editing marks that were introduced in this lesson. Follow these directions:

— First, in the top right-hand corner, write *Editing Marks* with a line under it.

— Then, copy the editing marks below. (Start on the top line. Skip a line after each item.)

1. An arrow ⟵ shows where a word or words should be moved.

2. **#** = Add space.

3. **] [** = Center the word or words.

4. **⌞** or **⁋** = Indent the line.

Keep this blue card in your Pocket Folder so you can find it easily. You will be adding more editing marks to your blue card from time to time. Memorize the marks so you can begin using them to correct the paragraphs you write.

 # MAKE A CUE CARD

A cue card reminds you what points to look for when you're checking a paragraph for mistakes.

When looking for format mistakes, ask yourself the six questions that are listed below. A cue card will help.

▼ Follow these directions to make yourself a cue card containing the six format questions. Use the lined side of a 4″ x 6″ white card.

—First, in the top right-hand corner, write *Check and Correct—1,* with a line under it.

—Next, center the word *Format* on the top line.

—Then, skip one line.

—Finally, copy these questions. Skip one line after each question.

1. Is the title centered?

2. Is there a blank line after the title line?

3. Is the first line of the paragraph indented?

4. Does each new sentence begin right after the sentence before it?

5. After the first line, does each new line start at the left margin?

6. Is the right margin uncrowded?

If the format of a paragraph is perfect, the answer to each of the six questions will be *Yes.*

PRACTICE MAKING FORMAT CORRECTIONS

▼ Read this handwritten How-to Paragraph, titled *How to Make Chocolate Cherry Milk*. It contains five format mistakes. Make the format corrections with editing marks using a colored pencil or colored pen. Use your white cue card and your blue card to help you.

	How to Make Chocolate Cherry Milk
	First, you measure a heaping spoonful of chocolate
	powder.
	Next, you pour the powder into an empty glass. Then, you
	fill the glass with cold milk and stir. Finally, you drop
	in a cherry.

HOW A HANDWRITTEN PARAGRAPH IS EDITED FOR FORMAT MISTAKES

Your format corrections on page 21 should look like the corrections below.

]How to Make Chocolate Cherry Milk [

⌊First, you measure a heaping spoonful of chocolate

powder. ⟵

⌐Next, you pour the powder into an empty glass. Then, you

fill the glass with cold milk and stir. Finally, you drop

in a cherry.

\#

EDIT YOUR OWN PARAGRAPH

In Lesson 1, you wrote your first How-to Paragraph, titled *How to Get a Glass of Water*. The assignment sheet is in your Pocket Folder.

Check to see if you made any format mistakes in that paragraph.

Make format corrections with a colored pencil or colored pen so your teacher can easily see your editing marks. Use your white cue card and your blue card to help you.

REVIEW OF LESSON 2 and editing marks

Circle the letter in front of the correct answer.

1. The format is the way a paragraph

   a. explains the title.

   b. sounds when you read it out loud.

   c. looks on paper.

   d. expresses the way you think.

2. The word *edit* means

   a. write a paragraph.

   b. finish writing your paragraph.

   c. choose a title for your paragraph.

   d. check and correct your paragraph.

3. You should indent the

   a. first line of your paragraph.

   b. last line of your paragraph.

   c. first word of every sentence.

   d. last word of every sentence.

4. The vertical line on the left side of the page is called the

   a. left edge.

   b. right edge.

   c. left margin.

   d. right margin.

5. Your white card containing a list of questions about format
   is called

   a. a paragraph.

   b. an example.

   c. a cue card.

   d. a subject.

6. The editing marks on your blue card will help you correct your

 a. pronunciation.

 b. written paragraphs.

 c. cue card.

 d. spoken paragraphs.

7. The editing mark that means "add a space" is

 a. #

 b. ∟

 c. ←

 d.] [

8. The editing mark that means "center the word or words" is

 a. ∟

 b. #

 c. ←

 d.] [

Number correct: _____ out of 8

Lesson 2 QUIZ Now your teacher will give you the quiz for Lesson 2.

✏ **ASSIGNMENT 2** Write two How-to Paragraphs. Each paragraph should contain four sentences. Your teacher will give you your assignment sheets.

Before you begin writing a paragraph, study the vocabulary words. Use the vocabulary words to help you as you write. (Or choose words of your own, if you like.) A flow chart is provided if you need it. For Paragraph 2a, look at page 25. For Paragraph 2b, turn to page 26.

VOCABULARY for Paragraph 2a:
How to Put Toothpaste on a Toothbrush

toothpaste	toothbrush
take off	tube
cap	squeeze

Fill in the flow chart by thinking about your instructions in steps.
Then begin writing your paragraph.

Title:

FIRST:

↓

NEXT:

↓

THEN:

↓

FINALLY:

VOCABULARY for Paragraph 2b:
How I Take a Nap

Whew! I need a nap!

asleep	pillow
couch	shoes
rest	yawn

Title:

FIRST:

↓

NEXT:

↓

THEN:

↓

FINALLY:

LESSON 3:
CAPITALIZATION AND PUNCTUATION

Capitalization means writing capital letters instead of writing lowercase letters. (**Lowercase** is another way of saying "small" letters.) **Punctuation** marks—like periods and commas—are marks between written words. They help make the meaning clear.

	CAPITAL LETTERS LOOK LIKE THIS
	lowercase (or "small") letters look like this

▼ The word "capital" means "first in importance." A capital letter is used as the first letter of the first word of a sentence. The capital letter tells you that a new sentence is beginning. It keeps the sentences from running together.

▼ The partner in this job of keeping sentences from running together is the punctuation mark called the period (.).

The mighty period (.) is as important as the capital letter. The period tells you that you've come to the end of a sentence. There are a number of punctuation marks, but this book will deal with only two: the period and the comma (,).

The comma has many uses. Here, you will use the comma after each FNTF formula word: *First, Next, Then,* and *Finally.* Why? To emphasize the importance of these words. (The formula words are extremely important: they organize our thinking.)

By now, you have written at least 3 How-to Paragraphs and learned to use 4 editing marks.

Time for the next step!

WHO NEEDS CAPITALIZATION AND PUNCTUATION? ▲▲▲▲▲▲▲▲▲▲▲▲▲▲▲▲▲▲▲▲▲▲

▼ Do we really need capital letters and punctuation marks? Try reading this paragraph without them.

	how i wash a car
	first i make sure the car is parked near a hose that is
	hooked up to a faucet next i get a bucket of soapy water a
	sponge and some old cloths then i wet the car with the hose
	and scrub it with a sponge and soapy water finally i rinse
	the car with the hose and dry it with the old cloths

Notice that the format of the paragraph above is perfect. It is easy to look at, but not so easy to understand.

The entire paragraph is written in lowercase. All periods and commas are missing.

This paragraph needs HELP. It looks like one long sentence, but it has no capital letter at the beginning and no period at the end.

Imagine trying to read a whole book without capital letters or punctuation marks!

C AND P RULES

Here is what the paragraph on page 28 looks like when it follows the rules of capitalization and punctuation—C and P, for short.

	How I Wash a Car
	First, I make sure the car is parked near a hose that is
	hooked up to a faucet. Next, I get a bucket of soapy water, a
	sponge, and some old cloths. Then, I wet the car with the hose
	and scrub it with a sponge and soapy water. Finally, I rinse
	the car with the hose and dry it with the old cloths.

▼ Most of us don't mind rules if they make sense. The paragraph above shows how C and P rules are used. But wait! Do they make sense? Examine them one by one. See if you can figure out the reason behind each rule. Discuss them with your teacher.

1. Each sentence begins with a capital letter and ends with a period. Why bother putting the period at the end of a sentence? Doesn't the capital letter tell us that a new sentence is beginning?

2. There is a comma after each formula word: *First, Next, Then,* and *Finally.* Why do you think the comma is there?

3. Take a close look at the title. One word begins with a lowercase letter and all the other words begin with a capital letter. Why do you think some words are capitalized in a title and some words are not?

4. Each sentence has a period after it. Then, why doesn't the title have a period after it?

5. In the paragraph above, the tiny word *I* is written with a capital letter, but the tiny word *a* is not. Can you think of any reason why the word *I* is always capitalized? Is the word *a* ever capitalized?

Proper formatting makes a paragraph pleasing to look at and easy to read. Proper capitalization and punctuation makes a paragraph easier to understand.

C AND P: WHAT TO LOOK FOR

▼ Here is what you find if a paragraph has correct capitalization and punctuation.

1. **The first word and all other words in the title begin with a capital letter, except small unimportant words.**

   Small words that do not add much to the meaning of the title, such as *for, to, a,* or *the,* are not capitalized. They are unimportant.

   Any small word, such as *Car, Do,* or *Go,* that adds important meaning to the title, is capitalized.

   Also, any small word that is part of a verb, such as *Get Rid Of* or *Turn On,* is capitalized.

2. **Each sentence begins with a capital letter.**

3. **Each sentence ends with a period.**

   Later, you may also write sentences that end with a question mark (?) or an exclamation point (!). For now, however, you will only write sentences that end with a period.

   A title is not a sentence. Do not put a period at the end of a title.

4. **Each sentence begins with a formula word, and that word is set off by a comma.** (In other words, a formula word always has a comma after it.)

5. **The letter *I* is a capital letter when it is all alone and it means *me*.**

6. **The formula words are in the correct order:** *First, . . . Next, . . . Then, . . . Finally, ...*

   This last rule helps you organize your thoughts as you write. It is put here as a reminder. Pay attention to the order of the formula words.

▼ Read this How-to Paragraph. Then, ask yourself the questions below it. You will find that the paragraph contains one or more mistakes in C and P (capitalization and punctuation).

	How to Draw A Smiling Face
	First, you take a pencil and draw a circle the size of a silver
	dollar on a piece of paper. next, you draw two dots for eyes in the
	middle of the circle Then, you draw a third dot for a nose between
	the eyes and slightly under them. Finally, you draw a curved line
	in the shape of a hammock under the nose and you have your
	smiling face

USE THESE QUESTIONS TO CHECK FOR C AND P MISTAKES

▼ Ask yourself:

1. Does each important word in the title, including the first word, begin with a capital letter?   _____

2. Do the unimportant small words in the title begin with a lowercase letter?   _____

3. Does each sentence begin with a capital letter?   _____

4. Does each sentence end with a period?   _____

5. This is a How-to Paragraph, so each sentence starts with a word from the FNTF formula. Does the formula word at the beginning of each sentence have a comma after it?   _____

6. Are the formula words in the correct order: *First, ... Next, ... Then, ... Finally, ...*?   _____

You're correct if you wrote *No* to questions 2, 3, and 4, and *Yes* to 1, 5, and 6. Turn the page to see how C and P corrections are made.

HOW DO I MAKE C AND P CORRECTIONS?

▼ Read below to learn how to correct the C and P mistakes in the paragraph on page 31. You will find that new editing marks are used.

	How to Draw ̸A Smiling Face
	First, you take a pencil and draw a circle the size of a silver
	dollar on a piece of paper. next, you draw two dots for eyes in the
	middle of the circle⊙Then, you draw a third dot for a nose between
	the eyes and slightly under them. Finally, you draw a curved line
	in the shape of a hammock under the nose and you have your
	smiling face⊙

A slash mark (/) is drawn through the letter *A* in the title to show that it should not be a capital letter.

Three lines are drawn under the letter *n* in the word *next* to show that it should be a capital letter.

Each missing period is inserted with a small circle around it, like this: ⊙.

Below is the same paragraph, but with different C and P mistakes.

VERSION 2

	How to Draw a Smiling Face.
	First, you take a pencil and draw a circle the size of a silver
	dollar on a piece of paper. Then, you draw two dots for eyes in the
	middle of the circle. Then you draw a third dot for a nose between
	the eyes and slightly under them. Finally you draw a curved line
	in the shape of a hammock under the nose and you have your
	smiling face.

Turn the page to see how the corrections are made.

This second version of the paragraph on Page 32 shows how to delete a period, how to get rid of words you don't want and put new words in their place (without erasing), and how to insert missing commas.

VERSION 2 CORRECTIONS

	How to Draw a Smiling Face .⌒̊
	First, you take a pencil and draw a circle the size of a silver
	Next
	dollar on a piece of paper. ~~Then,~~ you draw two dots for eyes in the
	middle of the circle. Then⌄you draw a third dot for a nose between
	the eyes and slightly under them. Finally⌄you draw a curved line
	in the shape of a hammock under the nose and you have your
	smiling face.

—A line with a loop ⌒̊ is used to delete, or take out, the period that does not belong. It can delete words also.

—A straight line is drawn through the first *Then*. (This is another way to delete.) The word *Next* is written above the deleted word to replace it.

—This editing mark ⋀ inserts the missing commas.

▼ Practice using the editing marks that were introduced in this lesson.

1. The title below ends with a period that doesn't belong. Use this mark ✐ to delete the period.

   How I Avoid Getting Soaked in a Rainstorm.

2. The sentence below is missing a comma. Use this editing mark ⋀ to insert the comma.

   First I button up my raincoat.

3. In the sentence below, the word *Then* should be changed to *Next*. Do this by drawing a line through the word that needs to be changed and writing the new word above it.

   Then, I open my umbrella and hold it over my head.

4. In the sentence below, one of the words should not begin with a capital letter. Use a slash mark to show that the letter should be lowercase.

   Then, When the rain starts coming down in buckets, I run for cover.

5. In the sentence below, two capital letters are missing. Make the corrections. Remember, three lines under a letter shows that it should be capitalized.

   finally, i step inside the nearest building.

 MAKE A CUE CARD

▼ Follow these directions to make yourself a cue card containing the five C
and P questions, plus the question about the order of the formula words.
Use the lined side of a 4"x 6" white card.

—First, in the top right-hand corner, write *Check and Correct —2*,
  with a line under it.

—Next, center the words *Capitalization and Punctuation* on the
  top line.

—Then, skip one line.

—Finally, copy these questions:

  1. Does each important word in the title, including the first word,
     begin with a capital letter?

  2. Do the unimportant small words begin with a lowercase letter?

  3. Does the first word of each sentence begin with a capital letter?

  4. Does each sentence end with a period?

  5. Does the formula word at the beginning of each sentence have
     a comma after it?

  6. Is the letter *I* capitalized when it's all alone and it means me?

  7. Are the formula words *First, . . . Next, . . . Then, . . . Finally, . . .* , in the
     correct order?

The answer to each question should be *Yes*.

ADD TO YOUR LIST OF EDITING MARKS

▼ In Lesson 2, you learned four editing marks and copied them on a blue card. (See page 19.) Now, add these six new editing marks to the list on your blue card.

5. A slash mark (/) through a capital letter means the letter should be lowercase.

6. Three lines under a letter means the letter should be capitalized. ≡

7. ∽ = Delete, or take out, a word, words, or punctuation mark.

8. ⊙ = Insert a period.

9. ⋏ = Insert a comma.

10. A straight line through a word or group of words deletes them. New words are written above the deleted ones.

PRACTICE MAKING C AND P CORRECTIONS

▼ The following paragraph, titled *How I Feed My Dog*, contains six mistakes in capitalization and punctuation. Make the C and P corrections with editing marks using a colored pencil or colored pen. Use your white cue card and your blue card to help you.

	How I feed My Dog
	First, i dump the old water out of the bowl.
	Next, I fill the bowl with fresh water. Then I check
	the dry food pan. finally, If the pan is empty I put
	a huge scoop of dry food in it,

HOW TO ADD MORE STEPS
TO YOUR PARAGRAPH ▲▲▲▲▲▲▲▲▲▲▲▲▲▲▲▲▲▲▲▲▲

So far, you have been asked to write How-to Paragraphs containing only four sentences. To add more instructions to a How-to Paragraph, simply add more sentences beginning with *Then*. This has been done in the paragraph below, which was written by a student.

▼ As you read the paragraph, underline the formula words. Notice how an extra *Then* is added to the FNTF Formula:

First, . . . Next, . . . Then, . . . Then, . . . Finally, ...

How to Groom a Horse

First, you tie the horse to a post or rail. Next, you brush the horse's body with a curry comb to loosen dirt and hair. Then, you brush the horse's face, body, and legs with a semi-stiff bristled body brush. Then, you clean out the horse's hooves with a hoof pick. Finally, you go over the horse's entire face and body with a soft finishing brush, and you comb the mane and tail.

In future paragraph writing assignments, try making your paragraphs longer by adding one or more sentences. Start each extra sentence with the formula word *Then*.

CHECK AND CORRECT

The paragraph below has many mistakes. All the mistakes are in format and in capitalization and punctuation (C and P).

▼ Take out your blue card and your two white cue cards. Read the paragraph. Use your white cue cards to help you find the mistakes. There are many. Use your blue card if you need help with the editing marks. Make corrections with a colored pencil or pen.

(This paragraph is an example of a longer How-to Paragraph. Notice it contains three extra *Then*'s.)

	How I Fix A Squeaky Door hinge.	
	First, I get a can of household oil. Next, i remove the	
	cap on the oil spout., Then, I point the spout at a movable	
	part of the squeaky hinge.	
	Then, I squeeze the can gently until a drop of oil comes out	
	of the spout Then, I point the spout at another movable	
	part of the hinge and squeeze the can again until another drop of	
	oil comes out. Then I continue doing this same thing until	
	all movable parts of the hinge are covered with oil. finally,	
	I swing the door back and forth to be sure the squeak	
	is gone.	

You should have made eight format corrections and eight C and P corrections.

Number correct: _____ out of 16

EDIT YOUR OWN PARAGRAPHS

▼ Now, go back and look at the two paragraphs you wrote for Assignment 2. Check and correct these paragraphs for C and P mistakes. Use your white cue card and your blue card to help you. Make corrections with a colored pencil or colored pen so your teacher can easily see your corrections.

REVIEW OF LESSON 3 and editing marks

Circle the letter in front of the correct answer.

1. The first word and all important words in the title should begin with a

   a. period.

   b. comma.

   c. lowercase letter.

   d. capital letter.

2. Do not put a period at the end of

   a. the title.

   b. the last sentence.

   c. each sentence.

   d. the first sentence.

3. Put a comma after each

   a. word in the title.

   b. formula word.

   c. margin.

   d. line.

4. The FNTF formula words stand for

   a. *Fist, Neck, Toe, Forehead.*

   b. *Faster, Neater, Thinner, Funnier.*

   c. *Forever, Now, Then, Finally.*

   d. *First, Next, Then, Finally.*

5. When you edit a paragraph, insert a missing period this way:

   a. ℋ

   b. #

   c. ↶

   d. ⊙

6. If you want to delete (or get rid of) a word,

   a. erase it.

   b. underline it.

   c. make the first letter a capital.

   d. draw a straight line through it.

7. You may also delete a word or punctuation mark with this editing mark:

   a. /

   b. ⊙

   c. ∿

   d. #

8. In this title, *How to Eat spaghetti*, you may use an editing mark to change the first letter of spaghetti to a capital:

   a. /

   b. ∧

   c. ☰

   d. ⊙

9. To make your paragraphs longer, add more sentences beginning with

   a. *Then, ...*

   b. *Finally, ...*

   c. *Last, ...*

   d. *First, ...*

10. This editing mark means "indent" the first line of the paragraph:

    a. ∟

    b.][

    c. ∿

    d. /

11. If you want to move a word or words to a new place, use

    a. an arrow, like this _____←_____ .

    b. a space mark, like this _____#_____ .

    c. a circle, like this _____⊙_____ .

    d. a delete mark, like this _____⌐_____ .

Number correct: _____ out of 11

Lesson 3 QUIZ Now your teacher will give you the quiz for Lesson 3.

✐ ASSIGNMENT 3 Write two How-to Paragraphs. Your teacher will give you your assignment sheets. Before you begin a paragraph, study the vocabulary words that go with the title. Use the vocabulary words to help you write your paragraph, or choose words of your own. A flow chart is provided if you need it. This flow chart has extra "Then" boxes to help you make your paragraphs longer.

For Paragraph 3a, turn to page 44. For Paragraph 3b, turn to page 45. Always write with a pencil. Put a line through any mistake.

VOCABULARY for Paragraph 3a:
How I Open a Jar of Mustard

> I need some mustard for my Brontosaurus sandwich!

clockwise	lid
firmly	twist
grasp	

Title:

FIRST: ↓

NEXT: ↓

THEN: ↓

THEN: ↓

THEN: ↓

FINALLY:

VOCABULARY for Paragraph 3b:
How to Open a Refrigerator Door

Will it open if I knock?

refrigerator	pull
hold	toward
handle	swings

Title:

FIRST:

↓

NEXT:

↓

THEN:

↓

THEN:

↓

THEN:

↓

FINALLY:

YOUR HOW-TO PARAGRAPH

LESSON 4: SUBJECTS

So far, you have learned how to check for mistakes in format and in capitalization and punctuation (C and P). The next step is to make sure your subjects and verbs are correct.

Each sentence needs a **subject** and a **verb**. The subject is the person or thing that does something. The verb tells what the subject does, or did, or will do. In the sentence, *The dentist pulled my tooth*, the subject is *dentist*; the verb is *pulled*.

▼ To keep things simple, we will use one of these three subjects for our How-to Paragraphs:

> *I,*
>
> *you,*
>
> or silent *you.*

EXAMPLE 1: *First, I remove my shoes.*

In this sentence, the person who does something is *I*, so *I* is the subject. (The verb *remove* tells what the subject does.)

EXAMPLE 2: *First, you remove your shoes.*

In this sentence, the person who does something is *you*, so the subject is *you*.

EXAMPLE 3: *First, remove your shoes.*

In this sentence, once again the person who does something is you, but this time the word *you* is invisible. When a writer (or speaker) gives an order or an instruction, the word *you* is often left out. Yet we understand that the subject is *you*. We may call this subject the *silent you*. (Some people call it "understood *you*.")

▼ Each of these three sentences is an order or an instruction. Notice that each contains a silent *you*.

Lock the door. (Meaning: *You lock the door.*)

Wash your hands. (Meaning: *You wash your hands.*)

Turn off the faucet. (Meaning: *You turn off the faucet.*)

PRACTICE FINDING SILENT **YOU**

▼ Each sentence below might be used as the first sentence of a How-to Paragraph. The subject either is *I, you,* or *silent you.*

(a) Read each sentence and underline the subject.

(b) If the subject is silent **you**, write **silent you** on the blank line after the sentence. Write either **I** or **you** if that is the subject. The first two have been done.

1. First, open the garage door. _____*silent you*_____

2. First, I peel the skin off twenty cloves of garlic with a vegetable knife. _____*I*_____

3. First, you face the camera and try to look relaxed. _____

4. First, I get the leash and call my dog. _____

5. First, collect any old newspaper articles about your favorite sports hero. _____

6. First, make sure the tiger has just been fed. _____

7. First, you scrub the orange under running water with a brush. _____

8. First, test the weight of the barbells before you try to lift them. _____

SUBJECTS: WHAT TO LOOK FOR

Here is what you find in a well-written How-to Paragraph.

1. **The subject in the first sentence matches the person in the title.**

    a. If the person in the title is *I*, the subject in the first sentence also is *I*.

    EXAMPLE a:

    Title: *How I Take Off My Shoes*

    First sentence: *First, I sit down.*

    (Notice that the word *I* is stated in the title, so *I* must be stated as the subject of the first sentence.)

    b. If there is no mention of *I* in the title, the subject in the first sentence may be either *you* or *silent you*.

    EXAMPLE b:

    Title: *How to Use a Tennis Racket*

    First sentence: *First, you grip the racket.*

    or

    First, grip the racket.

2. **The same subject is used in each sentence that begins with a formula word.**

    a. If *I* is used in the first sentence, *I* also is used in every other sentence that begins with a formula word.

    b. If *you* is used in the first sentence, *you* also is used in every other sentence that begins with a formula word.

    c. If *silent you* is used in the first sentence, *silent you* also is used in every other sentence that begins with a formula word.

	How I Make Blue Ice Cubes
	First, you get a clean, empty ice cube tray. Next, you
	turn on the faucet and run the cold water. Then, you fill the
	tray almost to the top with cold water. Then, you put a drop
	of blue food coloring in each cube. Finally, put the
	tray in the freezer and wait several hours.

USE THESE QUESTIONS TO CHECK FOR SUBJECT MISTAKES.

Ask yourself:

1. Does the subject in the first sentence match the person in the title? _____

2. Is the subject the same in each sentence that begins with a formula word? _____

Look at the next page to see how subject corrections are made.

HOW DO I MAKE SUBJECT CORRECTIONS?

Here is how to correct subject mistakes in the paragraph on page 50. One or more familiar editing marks are used and a new editing mark (called a caret, or insertion mark) is introduced. The caret looks like a tent ∧ and is used for inserting a missing word or words.

	How I Make Blue Ice Cubes
	First, ~~you~~ *get a clean, empty ice cube tray. Next,* ~~you~~
	turn on the faucet and run the cold water. Then, ~~you~~ *fill the*
	tray almost to the top with cold water. Then, ~~you~~ *put a drop*
	of blue food coloring in each cube. Finally, put the
	tray in the freezer and wait several hours.

—In the first four sentences, a straight line is drawn through the subject *you* to delete it. The subject *I* matches the person in the title, so *I* is written above each *you*.

—The subject *I* is inserted in the last sentence with a caret.

▼ Below is the paragraph on page 50, but with different subject mistakes. Can you spot the mistakes?

VERSION 2

	How to Make Blue Ice Cubes
	First, you get a clean, empty ice cube tray. Next, you
	turn on the faucet and run the cold water. Then, you fill the
	tray almost to the top with cold water. Then, put a drop of
	blue food coloring in each cube. Finally, put the tray in the
	freezer and wait several hours.

Notice that *you* is the subject of the first three sentences, but *you* is missing as the subject of the fourth and fifth sentences. Look at the next page to see how the corrections are made.

VERSION 2 CORRECTIONS

	How to Make Blue Ice Cubes
	First, you get a clean, empty ice cube tray. Next, you
	turn on the faucet and run the cold water. Then, you fill the
	tray almost to the top with cold water. Then, ~~you~~ put a drop of
	blue food coloring in each cube. Finally, ^you^ put the tray in the
	freezer and wait several hours.

—A caret, the insertion mark that looks like a tent ∧, inserts the subject *you* in the fourth sentence and the last sentence.

Here is the paragraph on page 50, but with a different subject mistake. What's wrong this time?

VERSION 3

	How to Make Blue Ice Cubes
	First, get a clean, empty ice cube tray. Next, turn
	on the faucet and run the cold water. Then, fill the tray
	almost to the top with cold water. Then, put a drop of
	blue food coloring in each cube. Finally, I put the tray
	in the freezer and wait several hours.

There is only one mistake in this paragraph. Look at the next page to see how the correction is made.

VERSION 3 CORRECTION

	How to Make Blue Ice Cubes
	First, get a clean, empty ice cube tray. Next, turn
	on the faucet and run the cold water. Then, fill the tray
	almost to the top with cold water. Then, put a drop of
	blue food coloring in each cube. Finally, I put the tray
	in the freezer and wait several hours.

—A line with a loop ⟿ is used to delete the subject *I* in the last sentence.

MAKE A CUE CARD

▼ Follow these directions to make yourself a cue card containing the two subject questions. Use the lined side of a 4" x 6" white card.

—First, in the top right-hand corner, write *Check and Correct—3* with a line under it.

—Next, center the word *Subjects* on the top line.

—Then, skip one line.

—Finally, copy these questions. Skip one line after the first question.

1. Does the subject in the first sentence match the person in the title?

2. Is the subject the same in each sentence that begins with a formula word?

The answer to each question should be *Yes*.

ADD TO YOUR LIST OF EDITING MARKS

In Lesson 3, you added six new editing marks to your blue card, bringing the total to ten. (See page 37.) Add this eleventh editing mark to the list on the blue card.

11. ∧ = Insert a missing word or words.

PRACTICE MAKING SUBJECT CORRECTIONS

▼ Read these How-to Paragraphs. Make subject corrections with a colored pencil or colored pen. Use your new white cue card and your blue card to help you.

	How to Wash Your Face
	First, you turn on the faucet and wet your hands with
	warm water. Next, lather your hands with soap. Then, rub
	your face thoroughly with your hands. Then, you rinse your
	face with warm water. Finally, pat your face dry with a
	towel.

	How to Set an Alarm Clock
	First, I pick up my alarm clock. Next, make sure the current
	time is correct. Then, press the "alarm set" button. Then, set
	the clock to the correct "wake up" time. Then, make sure the
	alarm button is "on." Finally, I put the clock back.

EDIT YOUR OWN PARAGRAPH

Now, go back and look at the paragraphs you wrote for Assignments 2 and 3. Check and correct these paragraphs for subject mistakes. Always make corrections with a colored pencil or colored pen.

HOW DO I CHOOSE A TITLE? ▲▲▲▲▲▲▲▲▲▲▲▲▲▲▲▲▲▲

▼ Suppose you are asked to choose a title for a How-to Paragraph. Which of these two titles would you choose?

How to Peel an Onion

How to Peel Vegetables

The first title is better. Why?

The title of a How-to Paragraph tells what the paragraph is about. The first title tells us that the paragraph will be about peeling one kind of vegetable, onions. Peeling one kind of vegetable is easier to write about in a single paragraph than peeling many different kinds of vegetables.

Peeling onions is a **specific topic**. *Specific* means talking about one thing. Peeling vegetables is a broad topic, which means that the paragraph should be about many different kinds of vegetables.

Here is another example of a title that is too **broad**. *Broad* means too large or too general.

How to Take Care Of a Pool

It is better to choose a more specific title, such as any one of these:

How to Replace a Diving Board

How to Clean a Pool

How to Change the Water in a Pool

SPECIFIC OR BROAD?

▼ Decide whether each title below is specific or broad. Write *S* for specific or *B* for broad on the line in front of the title. The first two are done for you.

1. _*S*_ *How to Do a Pushup*   5. _____ *How to Score a Home Run*

2. _*B*_ *How to Exercise*   6. _____ *How to Play Baseball*

3. _____ *How I Cook*   7. _____ *How I Ride a Motorcycle*

4. _____ *How I Mash Potatoes*   8. _____ *How I Get On a Motorcycle*

IS THE TITLE OKAY?

▼ Here are samples of How-to Paragraph titles that students have written. Many of these are good titles for a single paragraph. Some are too broad.

After each title, write *OK* if you think the topic is specific enough for a How-to Paragraph. Put an *x* if you think the topic is too broad. The first two have been done.

1. *How to Eat*   _*x*_

2. *How to Trap a Fruit Fly*   _*OK*_

3. *How to Arm Wrestle Your Brother*   _____

4. *How I Clean the Tires of a Racing Bike*   _____

5. *How to Draw*   _____

6. *How to Eat Spaghetti the Italian Way*   _____

7. *How to Use Computers*   _____

8. *How I Clean*   _____

9. *How to Feed a Rattlesnake*   _____

10. *How to Train a Parrot to Say "Hello"*   _____

REVIEW OF LESSON 4 and editing marks

Circle the letter in front of the correct answer.

1. The subject of a How-to Paragraph is

    a. always *I*.

    b. the first word of the sentence.

    c. always *you*.

    d. either *I, you,* or silent *you*.

2. If the title of your How-to Paragraph is *How I Shake a Person's Hand*, the subject in your first sentence must be

    a. *I*.

    b. *you*.

    c. *silent you*.

    d. *How*.

3. If the title of your How-to Paragraph is *How to Survive in the Desert if Your Water Canteen Is Empty*, the subject in the first sentence must be

    a. *you* or silent *you*.

    b. *Desert*.

    c. *I*.

    d. any of the above.

4. When you write a How-to Paragraph, use the same subject

    a. in each sentence that ends with a formula word.

    b. in every sentence.

    c. in each sentence that begins with a formula word.

    d. in each sentence that does not begin with a formula word.

5. The editing mark Λ for inserting a missing word or words is called

    a. a caret.

    b. a slash mark.

    c. a straight line.

    d. none of the above.

6. To delete a word or words, use

a. ✐

b. a straight line

c. either a. or b.

d. neither a. nor b.

7. Which of these three examples is the correct way to delete the word *you* and replace it with the word *I*?

a. First, ~~you~~ open the brown bag.

b. First, ~~you~~ open the brown bag.

c. First,]you[open the brown bag.

d. First, ~~you~~ open the brown bag.

8. In this title, *How To Braid Hair*, you may use an editing mark to make the first letter of *To* a lowercase letter, like this:

a. To

b. To

c. To

d. To

9. This editing mark means "add space":

a. ✐

b.] [

c. #

d. ∧

10. In the sentence below, the comma after the formula word is missing. Which is the correct way to insert a comma?

a. Next ∧ I reach inside the bag.

b. Next ⊘ I reach inside the bag.

c. Next / I reach inside the bag.

d. Next # I reach inside the bag.

Number correct: _____ out of 10

Lesson 4 QUIZ Now your teacher will give you the quiz for Lesson 4.

✏ ASSIGNMENT 4 This assignment has two parts. For Part One, you will be asked to make a Personal List of titles for How-to Paragraphs. For Part Two, you will be asked to write one paragraph. Your teacher will give you your assignment sheets.

Do Part One first. Then, turn to page 62. Study the vocabulary words that go with the paragraph title for Part Two. Use the vocabulary words to help you write your paragraph, or choose words of your own. A flow chart is provided if you need it.

VOCABULARY for Paragraph 4:
How I Get Rid Of a Fly

This always works with Pterodactyls!

around	follow
chase	newspaper
fly	swatter

Title:

FIRST: ↓

NEXT: ↓

THEN: ↓

THEN: ↓

THEN: ↓

FINALLY:

LESSON 5: VERBS

So far, you have learned how to check for mistakes in format, capitalization and punctuation, and subjects. The next step is to make sure your verbs are written correctly. As you know, each sentence has to have a **subject** and a **verb**. The subject is the person or thing who does something. The verb tells what the subject does, did, or will do.

In the sentence, *The gymnast flipped over the bar*, the subject is *gymnast* and the verb is *flipped*. The word *flipped* tells what the gymnast did.

VERB TENSE ▲▲▲▲▲▲▲▲▲▲▲▲▲▲▲▲▲▲▲▲▲▲▲▲▲▲▲▲▲▲▲▲▲▲▲

▼ The verb also tells **tense**. Tense expresses when the action occurs: in the past, in the present, or in the future. In the example sentence above, we can see that the action happened in the past because the verb *flip* has an *-ed* ending. *Flipped* is the past tense form of *flip*.

Here are some frequently used verb forms:

I *flip*	Present tense
I *flipped*	Past tense
I *will flip*	Future tense

The form used in a How-to Paragraph is the **present tense**. (Notice that the present tense does not have an *-ed* ending. It does not have a helping verb in front of it either, such as *will* or *would*.)

WHEN DO I USE THE PRESENT TENSE?

▼ Use the present tense

(1) when the action takes place now or on a regular basis (much of the time).

EXAMPLE: I speak to you from my heart.
(The action is happening now.)

EXAMPLE: I lock the door when I leave my house.
(The action takes place on a regular basis.)

(2) when a command or an instruction is given.

EXAMPLE: Call the fire department!
(Here a command is given.)

EXAMPLE: Wait until the rain stops before you go outside.
(Here an instruction is given.)

▼ In a How-to Paragraph, use the present tense of the main verb. Why?

The main reason is that the How-to Paragraph *gives instructions*. It tells how to do something.

The present tense is used because the action takes place *now* or *on a regular basis*.

VERBS: WHAT TO LOOK FOR

▼ In a correctly written How-to Paragraph,

1. **Each sentence contains a main verb (or verbs).**

2. **Only the present tense of the main verb (or verbs) is used.**

This rule works in How-to Paragraphs with all FNTF sentences (sentences that begin with a formula word).

PRACTICE SPOTTING VERBS IN THE PRESENT TENSE

▼ Read these sentences. The subject of each sentence is *I*.

(a) Underline the verb or verbs.

(b) If the present tense of the verb is used in the sentence, write
present tense on the blank line at the end of the sentence.
If not, write an **x**. The first two have been done.

1. I <u>waited</u> an hour for the bus. _____*x*_____

2. I <u>wait</u> for the bus every day except
Saturday and Sunday. _____*present tense*_____

3. Tomorrow, I will wait for it again. _____

4. I would wait for the bus on Saturday
if I needed to go downtown. _____

5. I play tennis. _____

6. Last summer, I tripped on a bicycle
wheel and broke my leg. _____

7. I chew sugarless gum. _____

8. I watch football on Monday night. _____

9. During my break, I grabbed a bite
to eat. _____

10. Maybe I will climb Mt. Everest
someday. _____

▼ Read this How-to Paragraph and answer the questions below.

	How to Make a Bologna Sandwich
	First, dip a plastic knife into a jar of mustard. Next, spread
	the mustard on one side of a piece of bread. Then, place a
	lettuce leaf over it. Then, lay one or two slices of bologna over
	the lettuce. Finally, put another piece of bread on the top.

USE THESE QUESTIONS TO CHECK FOR VERB MISTAKES.

Ask yourself:

1. Does each sentence contain a main verb (or verbs)? _____

2. Is the main verb (or verbs) in the present tense? _____

You're correct if you wrote *Yes* to both questions. Underline the main verb in each sentence.

▼ Here is another How-to Paragraph. Read it and underline the main verb or verbs in each sentence. Notice that these verbs are in the present tense.

	How to Sharpen a Pencil
	First, insert the writing end of the pencil in an electric
	pencil sharpener. Next, push the pencil forward and listen for
	the sound of the sharpener. Then, hold the pencil steady while
	the sharpener does its job. Then, remove the pencil. Finally,
	blow the extra shavings off the pencil tip.

 MAKE A CUE CARD

Follow these directions to make yourself a cue card containing the two verb questions. Use the lined side of a 4″ x 6″ white card.

—First, in the top right-hand corner, write *Check and Correct—4,* with a line under it.

—Next, center the word *Verb* on the top line.

—Then, skip one line.

—Finally, copy the questions. Skip one line after the first question.

1. Does each sentence contain a main verb (or verbs)?

2. In each sentence that starts with a formula word, is the main verb (or verbs) in the present tense?

The answer to each question should be *Yes.*

PRACTICE MAKING VERB CORRECTIONS

▼ The following How-to Paragraph is printed in three versions. You will find that each paragraph contains one or more verb mistakes. Make corrections with a colored pencil or colored pen.

VERSION 1

	How I Cross a Busy Street
	First, I stop at the corner. Next, I wait for the light across
	the street to turn green. Then, I look to my left and my right.
	Then, when all is clear, I step off the curb. Finally, I walked
	straight across the street to the other side.

VERSION 2

	How to Cross a Busy Street
	First, stop at the corner. Next, wait for the light across
	the street to turn green. Then, look to your left and your right.
	Then, when all is clear, step off the curb. Finally, I straight
	across the street to the other side.

VERSION 3

	How I Cross a Busy Street
	First, I will stop at the corner. Next, I will wait for the light
	across the street to turn green. Then, I will look to my left and
	my right. Then, when all is clear, I will step off the curb. Finally,
	I would walk straight across the street to the other side.

EDIT YOUR OWN PARAGRAPHS

Now, go back and look in your Pocket Folder at the paragraphs you wrote for Assignments 2–4. Check and correct those paragraphs for verb errors.

EXPANDED PARAGRAPHS:
ADDING EXPLANATIONS AND COMMENTS ▲▲▲▲▲▲

You have seen that one way to add steps to a How-to Paragraph is to add more sentences beginning with *Then*.

▼ Suppose you need to explain a complicated instruction, or you want to make a comment about it. This is easy to do. Simply put in extra sentences where you want to give more information or make a comment.

A seven-sentence paragraph may look like this:

First, ... Next, ... (Explain) ... Then, ... Then, ... (Explain) ... Finally, ...

We shall call this an **expanded How-to Paragraph**. To expand means to express at length or in detail.

▼ The paragraph on the next page, titled *How to Chew Gum When You're Not at School*, is an example of an expanded How-to Paragraph. The extra sentences, inserted mainly to give more information, are underlined.

As you read, imagine that Ms. Pebble, our Stone Age Time Traveler, has never chewed a piece of gum. Let's hope she would understand this paragraph!

A CLOSE LOOK AT AN EXPANDED HOW-TO PARAGRAPH

▼ Read this expanded paragraph to see how a comment and an explanation are inserted. The two extra sentences are underlined.

How to Chew Gum When You're Not at School

First, remove the wrapper from a stick of gum. Next, fold the gum in two and put it in your mouth. <u>The gum will fit more easily when it is folded.</u> Then, shift the gum with your tongue to one side of your mouth so the gum is between your upper and lower teeth. Then, move your jaw up and down in a biting motion to squeeze the sweet taste out of the gum. <u>Eventually, the sweet taste will disappear, and your jaw will get tired.</u> Finally, take the gum out of your mouth, wrap it in a scrap of paper, and drop it in a wastebasket.

Things to remember about extra sentences:

1. An extra sentence that is added to explain an instruction or make a comment does NOT begin with a formula word.

2. The main verb does not have to be in the present tense. It just has to make sense.

CHECK AND CORRECT

The paragraph below is an example of an expanded How-to Paragraph. This paragraph has four mistakes, one in each of the four editing categories you have learned so far: format, capitalization and punctuation, subjects, and verbs.

▼ Read the paragraph and underline the extra sentences that do not begin with a formula word. Then, make the corrections. (Use your white cue cards—*Check and Correct 1, 2, 3,* and *4*—and your blue card containing the 11 editing marks.)

	How to Thread a needle
	First, get a needle and a spool of thread. Next, decide on the
	length of thread you wish to use. To avoid tangles, it is wise to keep
	the length under three or four feet. Then, remove the thread you
	want from the spool by unwinding it and snipping it off with a
	scissors. Then, moisten one edge of the thread between your lips
	to bind the strands together into a smooth point.
	Then, moisten one edge of the thread between your lips to bind
	the strands together into a smooth point. Then, hold the needle
	between the thumb and first two fingers of your left hand. The eye
	of the needle should be pointing upward where you can see the
	opening. Then, insert the pointed edge of the thread into the eye of
	the needle. Finally, you would pull the thread halfway through the
	needle's eye and knot the two ends of the thread together.

EDITING SCORE: Number correct: _____ out of 4

Note that these instructions are for a right-handed person. How would you change the sixth sentence for a left-handed person?

REVIEW OF LESSON 5 and editing marks

Circle the letter in front of the correct answer.

1. The tense of a verb

   a. lets you know who the subject is.

   b. has something to do with stress.

   c. lets you know where the action takes place.

   d. lets you know when the action takes place.

2. In this sentence—*The tire rolled down the street.*—the verb is in the

   a. present tense.

   b. future tense.

   c. past tense.

   d. middle tense.

3. You should use the present tense of the verb in How-to Paragraphs

   a. to give instructions.

   b. to show that an action will happen later.

   c. to change the subject.

   d. to show that an action has already happened.

4. Suppose you are going to write a paragraph on how to make a pickle sandwich. Which beginning sentence should you use?

   a. First, you will open the pickle jar.

   b. First, you would open the pickle jar.

   c. First, you opened the pickle jar.

   d. First, you open the pickle jar.

5. It is easy to expand a How-to Paragraph by

   a. adding more sentences beginning with "finally".

   b. adding extra sentences that explain or comment on the instructions.

   c. taking out sentences that are interesting but not necessary.

   d. none of the above.

6. An extra sentence that explains or makes a comment

    a. does not begin with a formula word.

    b. is always very long.

    c. always begins with a formula word.

    d. is always very short.

7. Which editing mark changes a capital letter to a lowercase letter?

    a. three lines under the letter

    b. an arrow

    c. a slash mark through the letter

    d. three lines above the letter

8. Which editing mark inserts a period?

    a. $\wedge$

    b. $\odot$

    c. #

    d. $\llcorner$

9. Which editing mark centers a title?

    a. #

    b. (transpose mark)

    c. $\llcorner$

    d.] [

10. Which editing mark deletes, or takes out, a word or words?

    a. $\wedge$

    b. (transpose mark)

    c. #

    d. $\llcorner$

Number correct: _____ out of 10

Lesson 5 QUIZ Now your teacher will give you the quiz for Lesson 5.

⊛ ASSIGNMENT 5 Write two expanded How-to Paragraphs. For Paragraph 5a, turn to page 76 to study the vocabulary words. For Paragraph 5b, choose a topic from the Personal List. Write your own vocabulary words on page 77. An expanded flow chart is provided for each assignment.

(The flow chart has boxes at the right for extra sentences.)

VOCABULARY for Paragraph 5a: How I Put on a Jacket

arm   zipper

collar   sleeve

left   shoulder

right

Where's th[e] zipper?

Title:

FIRST:

NEXT: Explain or comment

THEN: Explain or comment

THEN: Explain or comment

FINALLY:

VOCABULARY for Paragraph 5b:

Title from your Personal List _____

Your choice this time!

Title:

FIRST:

↓

NEXT:

↓

Explain or comment

THEN:

↓

Explain or comment

THEN:

↓

Explain or comment

FINALLY:

LESSON 6: THOUGHT – PART ONE

▲▲ THOUGHT: DOES IT MAKE SENSE? ▲▲▲▲▲▲▲▲▲

You now know how to look for mistakes and make corrections in format, capitalization and punctuation, subjects, and verbs.

The next step is to check the **thought content**. Thought content is what the paragraph says, and whether it makes sense.

Your main job in writing a How-to Paragraph is to get your thoughts across to your reader. Otherwise the paragraph is just a lot of meaningless words.

THE MOST IMPORTANT STEP ▲▲▲▲▲▲▲▲▲▲▲▲▲▲▲▲

▼ Checking thought content is the most important step in writing and editing your paragraph.

This lesson will focus on three questions for checking thought content:

1. Does the paragraph stick to the topic stated in the title?

2. Is the paragraph organized?

3. Is the paragraph complete?

THOUGHT CONTENT: WHAT TO LOOK FOR

In a well-thought-out paragraph,

> 1. **The paragraph sticks to the topic stated in the title.**

In this book, the topic of a How-to Paragraph is always stated in the title.

If your title is *How to Put On a Backpack*, don't use the entire paragraph to explain how to adjust the straps on a backpack.

You've got to get the backpack on before you adjust it to fit! Adjusting the straps may be the final stage of the process.

▼ Now read the paragraph below. Does it stick to the topic stated in the title?

How I Feed a Banana to My Parrot

First, I rip a ripe banana from the bunch. Next, I hold the banana in my left hand and grasp the core with my right thumb and index finger. By core, I mean the tip that was attached to the stem. Then, I press with my thumb to bend back the core until it breaks away from part of the banana skin. Then, I peel one section of the banana skin away from the tip. Then, I peel back the other sections the same way. I let the strips of banana skin flop over my hand. Finally, when all the sections are peeled back, I remove the banana and toss the skin in the garbage.

There's a problem here.

As you can see, the paragraph does not fit the title. *Feeding a parrot* is not even mentioned in the paragraph.

A change is needed. The writer can either

(1) write a new paragraph to fit the title, or

(2) write a new title to fit the paragraph.

Let's take the easier route and change the title.

What will you choose as a title?
(Hint: Find the title by asking what the paragraph is mainly about.
Write your title on the line below.)

_____

The paragraph on page 80 is mainly about peeling a banana. If you wrote *How I Peel a Banana*, you chose a title that fits the topic of the paragraph. (Note that since *I* is the subject of the first sentence, you must put *I* in the title.)

PRACTICE FIXING THE TITLE

▼ Look again at the paragraph on page 80 and use editing marks to change the old title to the new title.

How many sentences does the paragraph on page 80 have? _____

Did you notice that two of the sentences do not begin with a formula word? These are extra sentences that add information and make the instructions clearer. Underline the two extra sentences.

▼ Now let's look at the second point for checking thought content.

2. **The paragraph is well-organized.**

It follows the FNTF formula, with or without the formula words. Is it necessary to always write the formula words? The answer is *No*, it's not.

Remember, a formula is like a recipe. If you cook the same thing again and again, pretty soon you know each step "by heart."

In the same way, you may no longer want to write the formula words in your paragraph. You can just keep them in mind.

From now on, you can choose to use formula words in one of three ways. On the next page, choose the way that works best for you.

CHOICE ONE

If you want to be on the safe side, continue writing the formula words, as in the paragraph below.

> *How to Check for Errors in Capitalization and Punctuation*
>
> *First, look closely at the title to make sure the first word and all important words begin with a capital letter. Next, examine the beginning word of each sentence to make sure it starts with a capital letter. Then, check to make sure each sentence ends with a period. Then, see that each formula word has a comma after it. (Make sure the formula words are in order.) Finally, use editing marks to make corrections if necessary.*

Notice that the only sentence that doesn't start with a formula word is the extra sentence. Extra sentences never start with a formula word.

CHOICE TWO

You may choose to include some of the formula words and leave out others, as in:

How to Check for Errors in Capitalization and Punctuation

First, look closely at the title to make sure the first word and all important words begin with a capital letter. Next, examine the beginning word of each sentence to make sure it starts with a capital letter. Check to make sure each sentence ends with a period. See that each formula word has a comma after it. (Make sure the formula words are in order.) Finally, use editing marks to make corrections if necessary.

CHOICE THREE

Maybe you'll choose to leave out all the formula words, like this:

How to Check for Errors in Capitalization and Punctuation

Look closely at the title to make sure the first word and all important words begin with a capital letter. Examine the beginning word of each sentence to make sure it starts with a capital letter. Check to make sure each sentence ends with a period. See that each formula word has a comma after it. (Make sure the formula words are in order.) Use editing marks to make corrections if necessary.

Whichever choice you make, don't forget to keep the formula words in mind to guide you.

PRACTICE ADDING WORDS WITH AN EDITING MARK

▼ Read the next How-to Paragraph. The organization is perfect. The formula words (*First, . . . Next, . . . Then, . . . Finally, . . .*) have been left out, but you can tell that the writer kept them in mind.

How can you put the formula words back into this paragraph? Decide where they belong and insert them with a caret ∧.

	How to Ring a Doorbell
	Go to the front entrance of the house. Look near the door to
	locate the doorbell button. The button is usually to the right of the
	door, about shoulder-level, either on the doorjamb or on the wall.
	Press the button with your index finger or thumb and listen for the
	sound of a bell or buzzer. A ringing or buzzing sound inside the
	house will usually tell you if the doorbell is working. After two or
	three seconds, remove your finger or thumb from the button and
	wait for someone to open the door.

▼ Underline the two extra sentences. Notice that two of the sentences do not call for a formula word.

▼ Now we're ready to move on to the third point for checking thought content.

3. **The paragraph is complete.**

In a complete paragraph, no important information is left out.

▼ The paragraph below leaves out a necessary piece of information. Can you figure out what information is missing?

How I Put On My Shoes

First, I sit down on a chair or bed with my socks on my feet and my shoes on the floor next to me. Next, I pick up my right shoe and use both hands to loosen the shoelaces. Then, I grasp the tongue with one hand. With the other hand, I hold the shoe above the heel. I pull with both hands to make the opening as wide and long as possible while I insert my right foot. My toe goes in first, then my heel. Finally, I put my feet on the floor, lean over, and tie my shoelaces.

As you probably noticed, the writer forgot to tell us how to put on the left shoe.

That step may seem obvious to most people. But our visitor from Stone Age times, Ms. Pebble, may have no idea what to do with the left shoe.

Try to fit it into somebody's pocket? Stuff it into a shoulder bag or a backpack? Feed it to the woolly mammoths?

Be complete when you give instructions.

HOW DO I ADD MISSING INFORMATION?

Here is how to use an editing mark, the caret ∧ , to insert the information that's missing. Write the missing information in the margin if it is several words. Or write the words above the caret if there is space. If it is only one word, write the word above the caret.

How I Put On My Shoes

Indent the first line.

→ First, I sit down on a chair or bed with my socks on my feet and my shoes on the floor next to me. Next, I pick up my right shoe and use both hands to loosen the shoelaces. Then, I grasp the tongue with one hand. With the other hand, I hold the shoe above the heel. I pull with both hands to make the opening as wide and long as possible while I insert my right foot. My toe goes in first, then my heel. ∧ Finally, I put my feet on the floor, lean over, and tie my shoelaces.

Then, I do the same thing with my left shoe.

. . . . WRITING THE HOW-TO PARAGRAPH

TRY IT!

▼ Read these phrases.

❏ of the gear

❏ the container

❏ that teamwork

❏ on the rim

☑ is tightly shut

The phrases in the list above contain missing information that belongs in the sentences below. Use a caret ∧ to insert each phrase in the sentence where it belongs. As you use each phrase, put a checkmark next to it. (The first one has been done for you.)

1. Be sure the freezer door. *is tightly shut*
∧

2. Put all aluminum cans in that is marked "Aluminum".

3. Tap the egg sharply of the frying pan.

4. Don't forget is the most important part of basketball.

5. Make a list you plan to carry in your backpack.

▼ Read the How-to Paragraph below. Then, ask yourself the questions that follow.

How I Tie Off a Braid

First, I brush my hair well so that it is easy to braid. Next, I separate the hair into three equal parts. Finally, I take the right section of hair and move it over the middle section. Then, I take the left section and move it over the middle. Then, I continue switching back and forth until the hair is too short. Then, I tie off the braid with a rubber band.

Use these questions to check for thought content mistakes. Ask yourself:

1. Does the How-to Paragraph stick to the topic stated in the title?

_____

2. Is the How-to Paragraph well-organized? Has the FNTF formula been used, with or without the formula words?

_____

3. Is the How-to Paragraph complete with no information missing?

_____

Answer to question 1:

No. The paragraph does not stick to the topic stated in the title. Tying off a braid is not the main thing. It's only a small part of the paragraph. What is the paragraph mainly about? Below is a list of titles. Decide which title best fits the paragraph and make the correction.

> a. *How I Braid My Hair*
>
> b. *How I Put On a Hat*
>
> c. *How I Keep My Hair Tangle-Free*

Answer to question 2:

Yes and **No**. The paragraph is well-organized, but the order of the formula words is wrong. Make the corrections.

Answer to question 3:

Yes. Within the paragraph, no important information is left out.

 ## MAKE A CUE CARD

Follow these directions to make yourself a cue card containing the three thought questions. Use the lined side of a 4" x 6" white card.

—First, in the top right-hand corner, write *Check and Correct—5*, with a line under it.

—Next, center the word *Thought* on the top line.

—Then, skip one line.

—Finally, copy the questions. Skip a line after each question.

1. Does the paragraph stick to the topic stated in the title?

2. Is the paragraph well-organized? Is the FNTF formula used, with or without the words?

3. Is the paragraph complete, with no important information missing?

The answer to each question should be *Yes*.

REVIEW OF LESSON 6 and editing marks

Circle the letter in front of the correct answer.

1. To make sure your paragraph is well-organized, check the

   a. subjects.

   b. verbs.

   c. thought content.

   d. capitalization and punctuation.

2. The topic of a How-to Paragraph is stated in the title. The topic is

   a. what the paragraph is mainly about.

   b. the first word in the paragraph.

   c. neither of the above.

   d. the last word in the paragraph.

3. If your How-to Paragraph is mainly about winning a bike race, your title should be

   a. *How to Buy a Racing Bike.*

   b. *How Ride a Racing Bike.*

   c. *How to Win a Bike Race.*

   d. *How to Ride in the Rain.*

4. To change the title of your paragraph, draw a horizontal line through the portion of the title you want to change and write the new words

   a. on the back of the sheet of paper.

   b. above the portion of the title you want to change.

   c. in the middle of the paragraph.

   d. on the very last line of the page.

5. By saying the formula words in your head while you write, it is easy to

   a. organize your paragraph.

   b. leave out important information.

   c. insert punctuation marks.

   d. insert capital letters.

6. You can be sure your paragraph is complete if

   a. the content sticks to the topic stated in the title.

   b. the paragraph is organized.

   c. the subject of the first sentence is *I*.

   d. no important information has been left out.

7. The correct way to insert missing words is

   a. Go to entrance of the house.

   b. Go to entrance of the house.

   c. Go to ^the front^ entrance of the house.

   d. Go to # entrance of the house.

8. Which editing mark changes a lowercase letter to a capital letter?

   a. three lines under the letter ☰

   b. a space mark #

   c. a slash mark through the letter /

   d. a caret ∧

Number correct: _____ out of 8

Lesson 6 QUIZ Now your teacher will give you the quiz for Lesson 6.

✏ **ASSIGNMENT 6**   Write two How-to Paragraphs. Vocabulary words for Paragraph 6a are on page 92. For Paragraph 6b, turn to page 93.

VOCABULARY for Paragraph 6a: How to Do a Push-Up

mat	count
muscles	body
breathe	push

Title:

FIRST:

NEXT: | Explain or comment

THEN: | Explain or comment

THEN: | Explain or comment

FINALLY:

VOCABULARY for Paragraph 6b:

How to Put On a Long-Sleeved Turtleneck Sweater

left arm	mirror
right arm	pull
head	waist

Title:

FIRST:

NEXT:

Explain or comment

THEN:

Explain or comment

THEN:

Explain or comment

FINALLY:

YOUR HOW-TO PARAGRAPH

LESSON 7: THOUGHT – PART TWO

▲▲ THOUGHT: DOES IT MAKE SENSE? ▲▲▲▲▲▲▲▲
(CONTINUED)

▼ Lesson 6 focused on three questions for checking the thought content of a How-to Paragraph:

1. Does the paragraph stick to the title?

2. Is the paragraph well-organized?

3. Is the paragraph complete?

TWO MORE POINTS TO THINK ABOUT ▲▲▲▲▲▲▲▲

▼ This lesson will focus on two more questions:

4. Is the paragraph clear?

5. Is the paragraph balanced?

In a well-thought out paragraph,

> 4. **The paragraph is clear.**

The instructions should make sense. They should be so easy to understand that even Ms. Pebble would be able to follow them successfully.

▼ Read the following paragraph. Are the instructions clear? Can you tell what action is being explained? Do you know what the title should be?

VERSION 1

> *First, get your sneakers. Next, sit down with your sneakers and your socks. Then, open one of them. Then, put in your foot inside. Then, put your other on in. Finally, tie your shoestrings in a bow.*

▼ In the next paragraph, the subject matter is the same as in Version 1, but the instructions are clearer.

VERSION 2

> *First, put on socks and sit down with your sneakers on the floor next to you. Next, pick up your right sneaker. Then, use both hands to loosen the shoelaces. Then, slip your right foot into the sneaker, toes first. Then, pick up your left sneaker, loosen the laces, and slip your left foot in. Finally, pull the laces tight on each shoe and tie them into a bow.*

What title would you give this paragraph? Write it on the line below.

_____

Now you're ready to move on to the final point for checking thought content.

5. **The paragraph is balanced.**

A balanced paragraph gives enough information to make the topic clear, and spreads the information evenly over the whole paragraph. Look at the four faces below and you'll get the idea.

SKETCH 1 — This drawing of a face is very skimpy. Too much is left out. Sketch 1 is like a paragraph that doesn't give enough information. It hardly carries enough weight to register on the Balance Scale, as we will see on the next page.

SKETCH 2 — This is a drawing of a face, but something is wrong. For example, the eyes are mere dots and one eyebrow is missing, while the nose and mouth are fully drawn. Sketch 2 is like a paragraph that is very skimpy in some parts and full of information in other parts. It is out of balance.

SKETCH 3 — This drawing shows all the main features and a small amount of detail to let us know that it's a picture of a young man's face. The parts are evenly distributed. There is no more detail in one part of the face than in any other part. Sketch 3 is like a paragraph that gets straight to the point. It says what needs to be said, but no more.

SKETCH 4 — This is the face of a young man, too, but more detail has been added. All parts of the face are clearly drawn. Sketches 3 and 4 both represent well-balanced paragraphs. Sketch 3 is like a paragraph that gets to the point quickly; Sketch 4 is like a paragraph that says what needs to be said and adds a lot of details. Which type of paragraph is better? That's a matter of taste.

THE BALANCE SCALE

On this page and the next page are four versions of a paragraph titled *How to Wash Your Hands*. Try rating these four paragraphs on the Balance Scale of **1**, **2**, **3**, or **4**.

> Too skimpy = a rating of **1**
>
> Out of balance = a rating of **2**
>
> Evenly balanced and straight to the point = a rating of **3**
>
> Evenly balanced with a lot of detail = a rating of **4**

Remember, a good How-to Paragraph rates either **3** or **4** on the Balance Scale.

YOU RATE IT!

VERSION 1

First, wet your hands. Next, add soap. Then, rub your hands. Finally, rinse your hands.

Balance Scale Rating _____

VERSION 2

First, turn on the sink faucet and let the water run until it is warm. You may have to wait 20 or 30 seconds. Next, wet your hands under the warm, running water. Then, turn off the faucet. Run your wet hands over a bar of soap, creating a lather. Rub your left hand with your right hand and your right hand with your left hand. Work the lather into your palms, fingers, cuticles, fingertips, and the backs of your hands. Finally, turn the faucet on again and rinse all the suds by holding your hands under the running water.

Balance Scale Rating _____

VERSION 3

> *First, go to the sink. Next, turn on the faucet. Then, run the water until it is warm. Finally, wet your hands under the running water, soap them, rub each hand all over with the other hand, and finish up by rinsing all the suds.*

Balance Scale Rating _____

VERSION 4

> *First, turn on the sink faucet and let the water run until it is warm. Next, wet your hands under the warm, running water. Then, soap your hands and rub each hand all over with the other hand. Finally, rinse the suds off your hands under the running water.*

Balance Scale Rating _____

BALANCE SCALE RESULTS

▸ Version 1 on page 98, which is the first *How to Wash Your Hands* paragraph, gets a rating of **1** on the Balance Scale—too skimpy.

▸ Version 2 is evenly balanced and rich in detail, and therefore rates a **4** on the Balance Scale.

▸ Version 3 contains all the necessary instructions but packs most of the important information in the last sentence. It is clearly "bottom-heavy" and deserves a rating of **2** on the Balance Scale.

▸ Version 4 is informative and evenly balanced, without much detail. It rates a **3** on the Balance Scale. Both Version 2 and Version 4 are well-balanced paragraphs.

HELP! IT'S TOO SKIMPY!

▼ Read this How-to Paragraph. The instructions appear to be clear and simple. But will Ms. Pebble have an easy time following them?

Can't I just yank it out?

	How to Change a Light Bulb
	First, get a new light bulb. Next, unplug the lamp. Then, take
	the old bulb out of the socket. Then, put the new bulb into the
	socket. Then, plug in the lamp. Finally, turn the light on.

This paragraph is well-organized, but it rates a **1** on the Balance Scale—too skimpy. Important pieces of information are missing such as: how to take the old light bulb out of the socket; how to put a new bulb into the socket; and how to turn the light on.

CORRECTING A SKIMPY PARAGRAPH

Here is an edited version of the paragraph on page 100. It now rates a **3** on the Balance Scale.

How to Change a Light Bulb

First, get a new light bulb. Next, unplug the lamp. Then, take
~~by unscrewing it.~~ screw
the old bulb out of the socket. Then, ~~put~~ *the new bulb into the*
clockwise, or to the right ∧   by flicking the switch
socket. Then, plug in the lamp. Finally, turn the light on. ∧

This means turning the bulb counterclockwise, or to the left.

As you can see, a lot of information had to be added to make the instructions clear. (When many words need to be inserted in one place, it's a good idea to keep them together by circling them.)

PRACTICE MAKING CHANGES WITH EDITING MARKS

▼ This paragraph below is well-organized but skimpy. Make changes so that it earns a rating of **3** or **4** on the Balance Scale.

	How to Make Peanut Butter Toast
	First, get some bread. Next, take out two slices. Then, put
	a slice in each slot. Then, press the lever. Finally, take out
	your toast and evenly spread the peanut butter.

YOU RATE IT!

▼ Read this new How-to Paragraph. Then, answer the questions on the next page.

	How to Kick a Soccer Ball
	First, make sure your cleats and your soccer ball are in
	good condition. Next, set your soccer ball on the grass. Back up
	several feet to give yourself a good running start. Begin running
	toward the soccer ball. Keep your eyes on the ball. When you are
	a couple of feet away, start looking in the direction of where you
	want the ball to go.

CHECK FOR THOUGHT CONTENT MISTAKES.

▼ Ask yourself:

1. Does the paragraph stick to the topic stated in the title? _____

2. Is the paragraph well-organized? Does it follow the FNTF formula, with or without the formula words?

_____

3. Is the paragraph complete? _____

4. Is the paragraph clear? _____

5. Is the paragraph balanced? _____

(How would you rate it on the Balance Scale? _____)

The paragraph *How to Kick a Soccer Ball* sticks to the topic and is organized, clear, and balanced (with a **3** rating). However, it leaves out an important instruction. If you answered *No* to the third question and *Yes* to the other questions, you are correct.

The writer left out the very last and most important step—kicking the soccer ball! Insert the missing instruction in the paragraph. Use a caret.

 ## ADD TO YOUR CUE CARD

▼ Take out your white cue card titled *Thought* and add the following two questions. Leave a blank line between the questions.

4. Is the paragraph clear?

5. Is the paragraph balanced?

The answer to each question should be *Yes*.

EDIT YOUR OWN PARAGRAPHS

▼ Now that you have completed your *Thought* cue card, go back and look at the paragraphs you wrote for Assignments 4 and 5. Check and correct those paragraphs for thought errors.

REVIEW OF LESSON 7 and editing marks

Circle the letter in front of the correct answer.

1. Ms. Pebble will understand your How-to Paragraph if the

   a. subject of the first sentence does not match the person in the title.

   b. subjects and verbs are incorrect.

   c. instructions are complete and clear.

   d. instructions are left out.

2. A How-to Paragraph is evenly balanced if

   a. not enough information is included.

   b. it has too much detail.

   c. it has almost all the important information in the beginning.

   d. it spreads the information equally over the whole paragraph.

3. A bottom-heavy paragraph contains most of the important information in the

   a. title.

   b. first part.

   c. margins.

   d. last part.

4. Use this editing mark to insert a period

   a. ⊙

   b. /

   c. ☰

   d. #

5. Which title is written correctly?

   a. *How to Climb a Ladder*

   b. *How to climb a Ladder*

   c. *How to Climb A ladder*

   d. *How to Climb a ladder*

6. To insert a word or words, use this editing mark:

   a. ∧

   b. ⌒

   c. neither of the above.

   d. both a. and b.

7. Which of these three examples is the correct way to delete a word and replace it with another word?

   a. Next, I spread the ~~ketchup~~ *relish* on the hotdog.

   b. Next, I spread the ketchup *relish* on the hotdog.

   c. Next, I spread the (ketchup) *relish* on the hotdog.

   d. Next, I spread the ~~ketchup~~ on the hotdog.

8. Use this editing mark to delete or take out a word or words:

   a. ∧

   b. #

   c. ⌒

   d. ≡

Number correct: _____ out of 8

Lesson 7 QUIZ Now your teacher will give you the quiz for Lesson 7.

✏ **ASSIGNMENT 7** Write two How-to Paragraphs. Vocabulary words for Paragraph 7a are on page 106. For Paragraph 7b, turn to page 107.

VOCABULARY for Paragraph 7a: How I Eat a Pizza

pizza box	plate
slice	catch the melted cheese
remove	mouth

Title:

FIRST:

NEXT: | Explain or comment

THEN: | Explain or comment

THEN: | Explain or comment

FINALLY:

VOCABULARY for Paragraph 7b:

How I Clean My Bedroom

Who needs all these clothes?

clothes	under the bed
floor	in the closet
fold	vacuum
drawer	

Title:

FIRST:
↓

NEXT:
↓
             Explain or comment

THEN:
↓
             Explain or comment

THEN:
↓
             Explain or comment

FINALLY:

LESSON 8: THE EASY NEXT STEP

▲▲ THE HOW-TO ESSAY ▲▲▲▲▲▲▲▲▲▲▲▲▲▲▲▲▲▲▲▲▲

▼ An **essay** is a written composition about a single topic. The topic is what the essay is mainly about.

Usually, an essay is made up of several paragraphs.

In a paragraph, all the sentences are related. In an essay, all the paragraphs are related.

You can say more in an essay than in a single paragraph. This is a big advantage if your subject is complicated. An essay gives you a chance to go deeper into the subject, to be more thorough. You can include more information, comments, and details.

Readers like to laugh as well as be informed. There is more room for humor in an essay than in a paragraph.

This lesson is about the next step: writing a How-to Essay.

Ready to go forward?

HOW-TO WRITE A HOW-TO ESSAY ▲▲▲▲▲▲▲▲▲▲▲▲

A How-to Essay consists of four or five paragraphs, or more if you have a lot to say.

Once again, the FNTF formula does the organizing for you.

BUILDING YOUR ESSAY FROM THE GROUND UP

The first thing construction workers do when they build a house is lay the foundation. Next, they build the frame, the structure that will hold the house together. The frame is usually made of wood. You can see through it. Then, the workers start filling in the frame. They add walls, ceilings, roofs, doors, windows, etc., until the house is complete.

Writing a How-to Essay is a little like building a house. Your title is your foundation. Your How-to Paragraph becomes the frame.

You build from there by filling in the frame with information, comments, and details.

We will call your original paragraph the "Frame" Paragraph.

FOLLOW THE STEPS

▼ The steps for writing a How-to Essay are listed below. You will see that each sentence of your Frame Paragraph starts a paragraph in your essay. On the following pages, there is an example of how this method works.

1. Decide on a topic for your How-to Essay. Choose a topic you're interested in and know something about.

2. On a sheet of lined paper, write a title that fits your topic.

3. Now it's time to begin your essay. Skip a line and write a How-to Paragraph based on the title. This will become your Frame Paragraph.

4. On another sheet of paper, write the title again. Skip a line and copy the first sentence of your Frame Paragraph. This sentence is now the beginning of your essay. Add more sentences to complete the paragraph.

5. To begin the second paragraph of your essay, copy the second sentence of your Frame Paragraph. Add sentences to complete the paragraph.

6. To begin the third paragraph of your essay, copy the third sentence of your Frame Paragraph, the sentence that starts with *Then*. Add sentences to complete the paragraph.

7. Continue until you use up all the sentences in your Frame Paragraph.

In this way, you can use any How-to Paragraph you like as a "frame" for an essay.

▼ Suppose you are writing an essay titled *How to Cross a Busy Street*. Here is your Frame Paragraph, which we borrowed from page 68.

How to Cross a Busy Street

First, stop at the corner. Next, wait for the light across the street to turn green. Then, look to your left and your right. Then, when all is clear, step off the curb. Finally, stay alert and walk straight across the street to the other side.

Before you begin your essay, think about your audience. Who is the person or persons you want to "speak to"? You can stick with Ms. Pebble, or you can write for your teacher or friends. You need to give accurate instructions to help someone cross safely!

Now why not make the How-to Essay fun to read by adding humor?

HOW THE METHOD WORKS

1 Use the first sentence of your Frame Paragraph to begin your essay. Then you can build from there, like this:

First, stop at the corner. *Stand at the curb and face the other side of the street. The corner directly opposite you is your destination. Look at the traffic light on that corner.*

2 To write the second paragraph of your essay, use the second sentence of your Frame Paragraph.

Next, wait for the light across the street to turn green. *A round red light or a bright red hand is a warning not to go. When the round red light turns green or the hand turns into a little gray man, prepare to move forward.*

3 The third paragraph starts with the third sentence of your Frame Paragraph.

Look to your left and your right. *Pay special attention to any car that has come to a stop immediately to your left. The driver may be thinking about turning the corner and may forget to look for you.*

4 The fourth paragraph starts with the fourth sentence of the Frame Paragraph.

> ***When all is clear, step off the curb and get going.** For a few seconds, you are on stage. Every driver on the street is watching you pass by. Walk briskly but don't run.*

5 The final paragraph begins with the final sentence of the Frame Paragraph.

> ***Finally, stay alert and walk straight across the street to the other side.** Step on the curb and breathe a sigh of relief!*

Notice the *Then*'s have been dropped at the beginning of the third and fourth paragraphs. It is O.K. to make minor changes in the sentences that you borrow from a Frame Paragraph. Remember, you don't have to put the formula words on paper. Just think of them when you write. It will keep the essay organized.

THE COMPLETED HOW-TO ESSAY: HOW IT SHOULD LOOK

As you can see, the format of an essay is similar to the format of a paragraph.

How to Cross a Busy Street

1 *First, stop at the corner. Stand at the curb and face the other side of the street. The corner directly opposite you is your destination. Look at the traffic light on that corner.*

2 *Next, wait for the light across the street to turn green. A round red light or a bright red hand is a warning not to go. When the round red light turns green or the hand turns into a little gray man, prepare to move forward.*

3 *Look to your left and your right. Pay special attention to any car that has come to a stop immediately to your left. The driver may be thinking about turning the corner and may forget to look for you.*

4 *When all is clear, step off the curb and get going. For a few seconds, you are on stage. Every driver on the street is watching you pass by. Walk briskly but don't run.*

5 *Finally, stay alert and walk straight across the street to the other side. Step on the curb and breathe a sigh of relief!*

ONE STUDENT'S ESSAY

▼ This next essay was written by a student who grew up in farm country. As you read the essay, consider these questions:

Is the writer interested in her topic? Do you think she knows much about the topic? Would a person who knows nothing about grooming horses learn something from reading this essay?

If we know and care about something, we can do a better job of writing about it. You've probably discovered that by now.

How to Groom a Horse

First, tie the horse securely to a post or rail. The horse should be standing on a relatively level surface in an area clear of machinery, dogs, or anything that might move suddenly.

Next, loosen any mud, dirt, or shedding hair on the horse. To do this, brush with a rubber curry comb in circular motions over the horse's body. Elbow grease is your best tool. Use the curry comb until you think all the hair and debris are loosened.

Then, brush the horse with a stiff body brush. Brushing the horse's coat in the direction of hair growth will remove all the dirt and loose hair that you brought to the surface with the curry comb. Brush the horse's entire body including the neck, chest, back, sides, stomach, hind quarters, and legs.

Then, use a metal or plastic hoof-pick to clean out all manure, straw, and rocks from each hoof. Facing the rear of the horse, stand at the horse's shoulder and slide your hand down the horse's back leg to the place right above the hoof. Lean on the horse while you put pressure on the lower leg so the horse will lift its hoof. Hold the hoof in one hand and use the other hand to clean it. Do all four hooves this way.

Finally, with a soft-bristled finishing brush go over the horse's entire body and face gently to sweep off any remaining dust or dirt. Comb the mane and tail with a regular hair brush for a finishing touch.

LOOKING BACK AT THE FRAME

▼ The paragraph below is the student writer's Frame Paragraph, reprinted from page 38, Lesson 3.

Underline the first sentence of each paragraph in the essay. Compare those sentences with the sentences from the original paragraph below. Notice how the student used each sentence from the Frame Paragraph to organize her essay. At the same time, she felt free to make changes to improve the essay.

How to Groom a Horse

First, you tie the horse to a post or rail. Next, you brush the horse's body with a curry comb to loosen dirt and hair. Then, you brush the horse's face, body, and legs with a semi-stiff bristled body brush. Then, you clean out the horse's hooves with a hoof pick. Finally, you go over the horse's entire face and body with a soft finishing brush, and you comb the mane and tail.

CHECK AND CORRECT

▼ Now is the time to think about everything you've learned and put it all together! Read the following paragraph. It has 10 mistakes, covering all the lessons so far. Find the mistakes (if you can!) and make corrections.

CLUE: Look for the following:

- two format errors
- five errors in capitalization and punctuation
- one subject error
- one verb error
- one thought error

		How to Practice Hitting a Baseball
		First. pretend somebody is guarding you closely. This is important.
		In a real game, a player on the other side will try to keep you from
		shooting the ball. Next dribble the basketball until you imagine
		you have an open shot. Then, Decide whether to take a jump shot
		or a set shot. Keep in mind that someone may be trying to block
		your shot.
		Then, you would shoot the ball toward the basket. finally, follow
		the shot to the basket to get the rebound in case you missed

Number correct: _____ out of 10

REVIEW OF LESSONS 1 through 8

Circle the letter in front of the correct answer.

1. The FNTF formula is
   a. *First, . . . Next, . . . Then, . . . Finally, . . .*
   b. *Finally, . . . Next, . . . Then, . . . First, . . .*
   c. *First, . . . Next, . . . This, . . . Finally, . . .*
   d. *First, . . . Now, . . . Then, . . . Finally, . . .*

2. The FNTF formula can be used when writing
   a. How-to Paragraphs.
   b. How-to Essays.
   c. both of the above.
   d. neither of the above.

3. You should indent
   a. the first line of your paragraph.
   b. every line of your paragraph.
   c. the middle line of your paragraph.
   d. the last line of your paragraph.

4 The format is the way a paragraph
   a. sounds when you read it out loud.
   b. looks on paper.
   c. expresses the writer's thought.
   d. none of the above.

5. The word *edit* means
   a. add sentences.
   b. write a paragraph or essay.
   c. check and correct your writing.
   d. read out loud.

6. When you write a paragraph or essay, make sure the title

   a. starts at the left margin.

   b. is centered above the paragraph or essay.

   c. has no blank line under it.

   d. starts at the right margin.

7. Put a comma

   a. at the end of the title.

   b. in front of each formula word.

   c. after each formula word.

   d. after each subject of the sentence.

8. Which title ends correctly?

   a. *How to Send an E-mail*

   b. *How to Send an E-mail,*

   c. *How To Send an E-mail.*

   d. none of the above

9. The subject of a How-to Paragraph is

   a. never stated.

   b. either *I, you,* or *silent you.*

   c. always *I.*

   d. never *I.*

10. If the title of your paragraph is *How I Put on My Snowshoes,* the subject in the first sentence must be

    a. *you.*

    b. *silent you.*

    c. *I.*

    d. snowshoes.

11. Which is an example of using subjects correctly?

   a. First, I open the bag. Next, you take out bread.

   b. First, you open the bag. Next, you take out bread.

   c. First, I open the bag. Next, Susan takes out bread.

   d. First, you open the bag. Next, I take out bread.

12. Which beginning sentence should you use to tell a person how to mop the kitchen floor?

   a. First, you get a mop and a bucket.

   b. First, you could have gotten a mop and a bucket.

   c. First, you would get a mop and a bucket.

   d. First, you got a mop and a bucket.

13. In checking the thought content of your How-to Paragraph, ask yourself:

   a. Does the paragraph stick to the topic stated in the title?

   b. Is the paragraph organized and complete?

   c. Is the paragraph balanced and clear?

   d. all of the above

14. The topic of a How-to Paragraph is

   a. stated in the title.

   b. what the paragraph is mainly about.

   c. both a. and b.

   d. neither a. nor b.

15. This topic is too broad for one paragraph:

   a. how to clean a desk.

   b. how to clean out your locker.

   c. how to clean.

   d. how to clean the screen on a computer monitor.

16. By saying the formula words in your head as you write, it is easy to

    a. avoid mistakes in capitalization.

    b. organize your paragraph.

    c. remember to indent the first line.

    d. keep the topic broad.

17. A paragraph that contains most of the important information in one part and very little information in the other parts is

    a. too broad.

    b. out of balance.

    c. both a. and b.

    d. neither a. nor b.

18. Your How-to Essay will be organized if

    a. you base it on a Frame Paragraph.

    b. the title states the topic.

    c. the subjects and verbs are correct.

    d. the topic is broad.

19. If you keep your audience in mind while you write your How-to Essay, it will help you to

    a. indent your paragraph.

    b. make your instructions complete and accurate.

    c. avoid mistakes in capitalization and punctuation.

    d. none of the above

20. Which is a correctly written title?

    a. *How To Build A Snowman*

    b. *How to build a snowman*

    c. *How to Build A Snowman*

    d. *How to Build a Snowman*

Number correct: _____ out of 20

Lesson 8 QUIZ Now your teacher will give you the quiz for Lesson 8.

✏ ASSIGNMENT 8 This is an essay assignment. You will need a Frame Paragraph. Look at the paragraphs in your Pocket Folder and choose one of your favorites to use as the Frame Paragraph. On a sheet of lined paper, make a clean copy of this paragraph.

On another sheet of lined paper, write a How-to Essay based on your Frame Paragraph. Make the instructions in your essay clear and complete. Think of your reader. Feel free to add humor.

Check and correct your essay before you turn it in. Use your white cue cards and your blue card to help you. (If the essay has other errors, your teacher will point them out to you.)

So long and happy writing!